1

I Cannot Reach the Stars

EPISODE ONE

Biing
Boong

THE SAKURA BLOSSOMS HAVE GONE FROM PINK TO GREEN.

IN THAT TIME, I'VE GOTTEN USED TO THE NEW UNIFORMS...

AND THE **STEEP SLOPE** IN FRONT OF THE SCHOOL.

Beeeng
Booong

BUT THERE'S STILL ONE THING THAT **HASN'T CHANGED** SINCE MIDDLE SCHOOL.

YUU!

RECRUITING'S GONNA BE OVER SOON!

HAVE YOU *STILL* NOT PICKED A CLUB YET?

I KNOW, BUT I'M STILL NOT SURE.

WHO'RE YOU TALKIN' TO?

YUP!

OH, NO ONE.

DO YOU HAVE CLUB ACTIVITIES NOW, AKARI?

JEEZ... YOU'RE SO INDECISIVE.

OR MAYBE I SHOULD CHANGE THINGS UP AND JOIN A CULTURE CLUB OR--

MAYBE TRACK AND FIELD... OR HAND-BALL...?

BAD-MINTON LOOKS FUN, TOO...

EXCUSE ME, KOITO!

KOITO YUU!

C'MON, JUST JOIN THE BASKET-BALL CLUB!

NAH, YOU'RE FINE!

AREN'T I A LITTLE SHORT FOR THAT?

AH...

YES?

STUDENT COUNCIL?

IF YOU'RE HAVING TROUBLE DECIDING ON A CLUB, WHY NOT JOIN THE STUDENT COUNCIL?

WHAAT? SOUNDS BORING!

OUR STUDENT COUNCIL ACTUALLY DOES QUITE A FEW DIFFERENT ACTIVITIES.

BUT BASKET-BALL...

IT'S FUN-- NOT SO DIFFERENT FROM A CLUB, TO TELL THE TRUTH!

OH, ARE YOU INTER-ESTED, THEN?

THAT WOULD BE A *HUGE* HELP!

HUH?

CAN I DO, LIKE, A TRIAL VISIT?

RE-ALLY?

AND I'VE BEEN LOOKING FOR SOME-ONE TO HELP US OUT. THANKS A LOT!

WHA?

STUDENT COUNCIL ELECTIONS ARE COMING UP SOON...

....

OH...

I'M SORRY...

BUT I CAN'T.

I...I SEE.

I GUESS A GUY LIKE ME ISN'T A GOOD FIT FOR YOU...

DON'T SAY THINGS LIKE THAT.

IT'S JUST THAT I...

YOU SHOULDN'T PUT YOUR-SELF DOWN FOR NO REASON.

I DON'T INTEND TO GO OUT WITH *ANYONE*, NO MATTER WHO ASKS ME.

NOW...

HM?

RUSTLE
RUSTLE

I'M SO SORRY!

IS SOMEBODY THERE?

Flinch

I SWEAR I WASN'T TRYING TO EAVESDROP OR ANYTHING! I JUST COULDN'T FIND A GOOD TIME TO COME OUT...

I'M SORRY!

!!

O-OF COURSE!

A RED RIBBON... SO SHE'S A SECOND-YEAR?

JUST KEEP WHAT YOU SAW A SECRET, OKAY?

AHH, OF COURSE! IT CAN BE PRETTY DIFFICULT TO FIND.

WHAT WERE YOU DOING OVER HERE, ANYWAY?

OH! UH, I WAS JUST LOOKING FOR THE STUDENT COUNCIL ROOM.

YOU REALLY KNOW A LOT ABOUT THESE THINGS!

I SUPPOSE SO.

ORIGINALLY, THE SPACE WAS USED FOR CALLIGRAPHY LESSONS, BUT LATER IT WAS GIVEN TO THE STUDENT COUNCIL.

THESE DAYS, I THINK THE ONLY ART CLASSES WE OFFER ARE MUSIC AND FINE ART.

RE-ALLY?

YOU MUST BE THE FIRST-YEAR WHO'S HELPING US OUT TODAY.

OH... YES!

HERE WE ARE.

SHE'S BEEN MORE POPULAR THAN THE STUDENT COUNCIL PRESIDENT SINCE HER FRESHMAN YEAR.

OH, I'VE HEARD THAT NAME BEFORE.

HER NAME'S NANAMI-SENPAI.

SHE'S NICE, AND PRETTY, AND SUPER GOOD AT HER JOB!

BUT SHE WAS REALLY COOL!

KOYOMI, IF YOU JOIN A CLUB, YOU MIGHT MEET SOMEONE, TOO!

I'D PREFER SOMEONE OLDER...

SERIOUSLY?

I MEAN, YOU DID CHOOSE THIS SCHOOL JUST TO GET NEAR HIM.

OH MAN, SENPAI WAS AS COOL AS EVER YESTERDAY!!

Clench

WHEN YOU SAID "A COOL SENPAI," I WAS SURE IT'D BE A GUY!

AS IF I NEED TO ASK...

HOW WAS BASKETBALL CLUB, AKARI?

UGH... I THOUGHT WE WERE FINALLY GONNA GET A LOVE STORY OUT OF YUU...

YOU SHOULD'VE KNOWN BETTER THAN THAT.

ON THE DAY OF MY MIDDLE SCHOOL GRADUATION, A BOY ASKED ME OUT.

I STILL HAVEN'T ANSWERED HIM.

I THOUGHT ABOUT ASKING AKARI AND KOYOMI FOR ADVICE...

BUT...

THAT SENPAI ...

"I DON'T INTEND TO GO OUT WITH ANYONE, NO MATTER WHO ASKS ME."

SO, TOUKO...

BUT SERIOUSLY, THE BOY YOU TURNED DOWN TOLD ME HIMSELF.

HOW'D YOU KNOW ABOUT THAT, SAYAKA...?

WAIT, WHAT? WHY?

OH, PLEASE. DON'T UNDER-ESTIMATE MY INTELLIGENCE NETWORK.

IS IT *TRUE* THAT SOMEONE ASKED YOU OUT AGAIN?

REALLY... IF THEY'RE JUST ASKING FOR *KICKS*, WHAT WOULD THEY DO IF I ACTUALLY SAID "YES"?

YEAH, LIKE *THAT* WOULD EVER HAPPEN.

WHOA!

YOU'VE GOT NOTH-ING TO LOSE BY TRYING.

THERE'S BEEN AT LEAST TEN SINCE WE STARTED HIGH SCHOOL, RIGHT?

BUT YOU KNOW, I DON'T THINK IT'S ALL THAT EMBARRASS-ING TO HAVE BEEN TURNED DOWN BY TOUKO.

OKAY, YOU CAN *STOP* TALKING NOW.

WHA --?!

S-SO, THAT SORT OF THING REALLY DOES HAPPEN...?

SHE'S EVEN HAD *GIRLS* CONFESS TO HER BEFORE!

I SEE.

IS THERE A REASON FOR THAT, OR...?

A REASON, HUH? NOT PARTICULARLY, IT'S JUST...

I FEEL A LITTLE BAD ABOUT IT...

BUT I'M JUST NOT INTERESTED.

OKAY, PUTTING THAT ASIDE...

HASN'T THERE BEEN ANYBODY WHO'S CAUGHT YOUR EYE?

ALTHOUGH THEY ALL SAY THEY LIKE ME...

NONE OF THEIR CONFESSIONS HAVE MADE MY HEART POUND.

UM...

ABOUT THAT--

EXCUSE ME!

OH, ARE YOU A FRESHMAN?

WELCOME!

I'M INTERESTED IN JOINING THE STUDENT COUNCIL...

I'd like to hear your answer soon...

Is it all right if I call you after school tomorrow?

I understand. Sorry to keep you waiting so long. Tomor!

明日　明日中　送信
あした　明日

あ　か
な　は
や　ら
わ　・?!

SW AAK

SHE'S NOT HERE YET...

Ha!

HM?

I GUESS IT WAS SILLY TO RUN ALL THE WAY HERE...

BUT... I THOUGHT IF I COULD ASK HER ABOUT IT...

Ha! Ha!

YOU'RE EARLY, KOITO-SAN.

THAT'S QUITE ADMIRABLE.

SENPAI...!

HMM?

SAYAKA SAID SHE HAS TO TAKE CARE OF SOMETHING AT HOME, SO SHE WON'T BE COMING TODAY.

IT'LL JUST BE YOU AND ME...

UMM, SENPAI!

ERR, WELL...

WH...WHAT ENDED UP HAPPENING WITH THAT BOY?

THE FIRST-YEAR WHO CAME EARLIER?

OH, HIM?

!

SLIDE

BUT HOW CAN I ASK...?

THIS ISN'T WHAT I WANTED TO TALK ABOUT...

HE'S GOING TO BE HELPING US OUT.

HE SAID HE'LL COME STARTING TOMOR-ROW.

OH, THAT'S GREAT.

MAYBE HE'LL BE ABLE TO HELP YOU WITH SOME OF YOUR DUTIES, TOO.

SURE, SOUNDS GOOD.

SO YOU HAVE TO RESPOND TO HIS CONFESSION...

STILL, IT'S NOT LIKE I KNOW HIM, SO...

I'M NOT SURE I CAN HELP YOU DECIDE WHAT TO DO.

HE MUST BE PRETTY SERIOUS IF HE'S BEEN WAITING FOR A MONTH NOW.

OH, IT'S NOT THAT...

I ALREADY KNOW WHAT I'M GOING TO SAY.

OH?

"NONE OF THEM HAVE MADE MY HEART POUND."

I THOUGHT MAYBE *YOU* WOULD UNDERSTAND, NANAMI-SENPAI.

SO...

BUT...

I COULDN'T ASK MY FRIENDS FOR ADVICE ABOUT IT...

PAT

MN?

IT MUST HAVE BEEN HARD TO FEEL LIKE YOU HAD TO FALL IN LOVE.

SMILE

YOU TOO...?

EVERYONE LOVES TALKING ABOUT LOVE AND ROMANCE...

SOMETIMES I WONDER IF THERE'S SOMETHING *WRONG* WITH ME.

I HOPE I CAN EXPLAIN MY FEELINGS AS CLEARLY AS YOU DO...

KLATTER

Incoming call

VRRZZZ

!

IS THAT HIM?

VRRZZ

IT'S ALL RIGHT.

VRZZ

VRZZ

VRZZ

VRZZ

YOU'LL BE FINE.

JUST HONESTLY TELL HIM HOW YOU FEEL...

THE SAME WAY HE TOLD YOU.

SQUEEZE

YEAH... YOU, TOO.

THANK YOU.

THANK YOU SO MUCH.

I DON'T KNOW HOW I WOULD'VE DONE IT IF YOU HADN'T BEEN HERE, SENPAI.

PhEW...

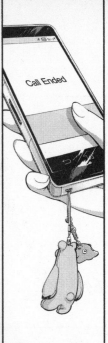

Call Ended

UM...

SENPAI?

IT'S NOT REALLY A BIG DEAL... THIS ROOM'S FULL OF 'EM.

THIS IS THE ALLY THE STUDENT COUNCIL HAS BEEN LONGING FOR...

A PERSON WHO CAN FIGHT OFF BUGS!!

CLENCH

WHACK

(Bloom Into You)

2

First Blush

EPISODE TWO

"I THINK
I MIGHT
BE FALLING
IN LOVE
WITH
YOU."

HN?

UMM... NANAKO-SENPAI...?

FWIP

AH...!

I'M SORRY, KOITO-SAN.

ANYWAY... TIME TO GET TO WORK!

I DIDN'T MEAN TO BLURT OUT SOMETHING SO WEIRD.

JUST DON'T WORRY ABOUT IT, OKAY?

AH HA HA!

......

blub
blub

STILL, SOMETHING ABOUT THE WAY SHE WAS LOOKING AT ME...

I MEAN, WE ARE BOTH GIRLS...

I'VE GOT NOTHING TO WORRY ABOUT.

plip

SHE HASN'T REALLY SAID *ANYTHING* SINCE THAT DAY...

MAYBE I WAS READING INTO IT *TOO* MUCH?

C'MON, I'VE BEEN BUSY WITH MY *CLUB ACTIVITIES* AND STUFF!

PRESI-DENT KUZE...

WHAT DO YOU THINK YOU'RE DOING? YOU CAN'T JUST WALTZ IN HERE AFTER BARELY SHOWING YOUR FACE AROUND HERE *THE WHOLE SEMESTER!*

IT'S OKAY! IT DIDN'T TAKE *TOO* LONG TO GET USED TO EVERY-THING.

IF I GET LUCKY, MAYBE I'LL BECOME AN OFFICER SOMEDAY!

HEY, FIRST-YEARS! SORRY YOU GOT PLUNGED INTO ALL THIS SO SUDDENLY.

KOITO, RIGHT?

MAKI AND...

YOU *REALLY* SAVED OUR BUTTS!

THAT'S RIGHT! ISN'T SHE THE FUTURE STUDENT COUNCIL *PRESI-DENT?*

WELL, THAT'S UP TO TOUKO OVER THERE.

WELL, *EXCU-USE ME* FOR BELIEVING IN YOU!

WHY DON'T WE GET SOME MORE SODA?

HEY!

THAT HASN'T BEEN DECIDED YET!

BUT THE ELECTIONS ARE STARTING SOON.

SURE, BUT YOU'RE RUNNING FOR OFFICE, *RIGHT?* IT'S PRACTICALLY YOURS AL-READY.

YOU KNOW IT'S NOT THAT SIMPLE.

IS IT JUST ME, OR DOES TOUKO SEEM TO BE IN A GOOD MOOD?

YOU THINK?

WHAT ABOUT YOU, SAEKI-SENPAI? WOULDN'T *YOU* LIKE TO BE PRESIDENT?

NAH, I'M ALL SET.

SINCE A CERTAIN SOMEONE PUSHED ALL HIS DUTIES OFF ON HER.

I MEAN... EVEN AS A FIRST-YEAR SHE WAS *BASICALLY* THE FACE OF THE STUDENT COUNCIL.

THERE'S *NO WAY* NANAMI-SENPAI WON'T BE NOMINATED FOR PREZ, RIGHT?

Phoo!♪

LIKE ALWAYS...

I'M JUST HAPPY TO STAY BY TOUKO'S SIDE AND SUPPORT HER.

Bleh!

OH MAN, THAT'S A TOUGH ONE.

THIS SUCKS...!

Year 1
Class 1

I THINK I'D HELP HER HAND OUT FLIERS AND MAKE POSTERS AND STUFF.

UM...

WHAT DOES A CAMPAIGN MANAGER EVEN DO?

THAT KIND OF STUFF'S PRETTY HARD FOR YOU, ISN'T IT?

THINGS LIKE PUBLIC SPEAK-ING.

THAT IS PRETTY BAD.

UGH...

ACK!

I'D ALSO HAVE TO GIVE A CAMPAIGN SPEECH IN FRONT OF THE WHOLE SCHOOL.

YEAH, I KNOW, BUT...

BUT I GUESS IT'S NOT TOO BAD IF THAT'S THE ONLY THING YOU HAVE TO DO.

WELL, THAT DOESN'T EXACTLY SOUND FUN...

SHE'S REALLY TAKEN A LIKING TO YOU, HUH?

IT SEEMS LIKE A LOT OF RESPONSIBILITY...

I DON'T KNOW IF I CAN DO IT.

I GUESS, THOUGH, I DON'T KNOW WHY...

I *TRIED*, BUT NANAMI-SENPAI WON'T GIVE UP ON THE IDEA!

WHY NOT JUST TELL HER NO?

Top Grade Results: 2nd Years

1 Class 1 Nanami Touko — 489
2 Class 1 Sanae Sayaka — 482
3 Class 3 Yamanaka Nobuyuki
4 Class 2 Mitarai Tooru
5 Class

NANAMI-SENPAI ALREADY HAS SANAE-SENPAI, DOESN'T SHE?

APPARENTLY, THEY'VE HELD THE TOP RANKINGS EVER SINCE STARTING SCHOOL HERE...

"SHE'S REALLY TAKEN A LIKING TO YOU, HUH?"

SHE SHOULD BE THE LOGICAL CHOICE FOR NANAMI-SENPAI, BUT...

THEY STAND OUT JUST BY WALKING SIDE BY SIDE.

NO WAY!

swish

swish

YOU'RE IN *FINE* FORM TODAY.

I SAID I'M SORRY! HOW CAN I MAKE IT UP TO YOU?

SAYAKA?

I GUESS I JUST *ASSUMED* I WOULD BE YOUR CAMPAIGN MANAGER.

I DON'T KNOW...

I KNOW, I SHOULD HAVE TALKED TO YOU ABOUT IT FIRST. I REALLY AM SORRY!

SEE?

I MEAN, SHE'S A PRETTY CAPABLE PERSON...

BUT I STILL WANT KOITO-SAN TO BE MY CAMPAIGN MANAGER.

SO IT'S NOT THAT I DOUBT SHE'S UP TO THE TASK, BUT...

I STILL DON'T GET IT.

......

WHY'S THAT?

YOU ARE TAKING THE ELECTION SERI-OUSLY, RIGHT?

YOU'RE NOT LETTING YOUR GUARD DOWN JUST BECAUSE EVERYONE'S SAYING YOU'LL WIN, ARE YOU?

I AM TAKING IT SERI-OUSLY.

I JUST... THINK IT MAKES SENSE TO HAVE A FIRST-YEAR BE MY CAMPAIGN MANAGER.

I MEAN, MAY *IS* AWFULLY EARLY TO HOLD THE ELECTION...

THEY MIGHT END UP FEELING LIKE IT HAS NOTHING TO DO WITH THEM.

I SUP-POSE NOT...

BUT THEY'LL PAY ATTENTION IF THEY SEE A FELLOW FIRST-YEAR STANDING AT THE PODIUM.

SO THE FIRST-YEARS WON'T KNOW THE CANDI-DATES VERY WELL, WILL THEY?

THAT WAY, IT'LL SHOW I'M WILLING TO LISTEN TO EVERYBODY'S OPINIONS!

AND INSTEAD OF HAVING HER SING MY PRAISES THE WHOLE TIME...

I'M GOING TO ASK KOITO-SAN TO GIVE HER HONEST ASSESS-MENT OF ME.

NEXT MATCH IS START-ING!

PRETTY GOOD, DON'T YOU THINK?

SO, I THINK FIGHTING THROUGH THE ELECTION TOGETHER WILL BE A GOOD WAY TO BUILD TRUST.

THEN... IN OTHER WORDS...

YOU WANT YOUR BOND WITH *HER* TO BE DEEPER THAN OURS?

phWEEE

SAYAKA!

bwomp

BWAAM

PWOMP

T...
TOUKO!

Yay!

Woo!

WE WON!

TOUKO, SAEKI-SAN, YOU WERE BOTH AMAZING!

YEAH, YOU WERE LIKE PERFECTLY IN SYNC!

P-WEEE

TWONK

OKAY THEN.

I'LL DO MY BEST.

Candidate:
Year 2, Class 1 Nanami Touko

学級担任 辻 浮子
学作工任 小振 貴7

Manager:
Year 1, Class 1 Koito Yuu

学級担任 青山 慈

WELL, WE'RE NOW OFFICIALLY PARTNERS FOR THE ELECTION, KOITO-SAN.

LET'S GIVE IT EVERY-THING WE'VE GOT!

YOU KNOW, I HAD NO IDEA YOU COULD BE SO *PUSHY,* NANAMI-SENPAI.

I JUST REALLY WANTED YOU TO DO IT!

I'LL DO AS MUCH AS I CAN...

BUT YOU'RE PROBABLY GONNA HAVE TO SHOW ME THE ROPES, OKAY?

BUT WHY ME...?

NO WORRIES!

THE OTHER DAY... WHAT WAS *THAT* ALL ABOUT?

THE OTHER DAY?

SO, UM...

YES?

THAT WAS...

"I THINK I MIGHT BE FALLING IN LOVE WITH YOU"...

THAT.

HMM...

I'M REALLY SORRY IF I MADE YOU UNCOMFORTABLE.

ding
ding

ding

I MEAN, I KNOW YOU DIDN'T MEAN IT IN A WEIRD WAY OR ANYTHING!

OH, NO!

I WASN'T THINKING...

IT KIND OF JUST... CAME OUT...

CHA-CLANK

CHA-CLANK

ding

ding

WHEN I SAID "LOVE"...

I MEANT THAT KIND OF LOVE.

ding

ding

CHA-CLANK

WHEN I'M WITH YOU, MY *HEART POUNDS*...

THOUGH I'VE NEVER FELT THAT WAY TOWARD *ANYONE* BEFORE.

chatter

chatter

chatter

chatter

chatter

WHAT SHOULD I DO?

I...

SHOULDN'T *I* BE THE ONE ASKING THAT QUESTION?

(**Bloom Into You**)

HEY! YOU'RE LATE, TOUKO!

THANKS!

AH HA HA!

OF COURSE! I THOUGHT YOU MIGHT NEED SOME HELP.

I'M REALLY GLAD YOU CAME, MAKI-KUN.

WOW, THERE'RE SO MANY PEOPLE HERE TO HELP WITH THE ELECTIONS.

AT LONG LAST, OUR LEADING LADY MAKES AN ENTRANCE!

I SAID I'M SORRY!

SORRY TO KEEP YOU ALL WAITING!

THANKS FOR COMING TODAY, EVERYONE.

SINCE ELECTION ACTIVITIES START TO-MORROW...

I THOUGHT IT WOULD BE A GOOD IDEA TO MEET FACE-TO-FACE BEFOREHAND AND...

3

Campaigning for Love

EPISODE THREE

GOOD WORK.

SEE YOU TOMOR-ROW!

chatter

chatter

KOITO-SAN.

FAN-TASTIC WORK TODAY--

CAN I TALK TO YOU?

DON'T WORRY ABOUT IT. IT'S REALLY OKAY.

I WANTED TO APOLOGIZE ABOUT THE OTHER DAY.

STILL...

I...

I REALLY AM SORRY.

I JUST WANTED TO WORK TOGETHER, AS FRIENDS...

ARE YOU OKAY WITH THAT?

BUT...

THAT WASN'T WHY I ASKED YOU TO BE MY CAMPAIGN MANAGER, KOITO-SAN.

REALLY?

WELL, I ALREADY TOLD YOU YES...

AND SAEKI-SENPAI IS COUNTING ON ME, TOO.

UM... OKAY. SURE.

THANK YOU!

SO, YEAH. I'LL DO IT.

I'M REALLY NOT UPSET AT ALL.

I'LL GO GRAB ANOTHER FROM THE TEACHER IN CHARGE OF THE ELECTION COMMITTEE.

TOUKO?

THIS ONE DOESN'T HAVE A STAMP ON IT.

OH, DID THEY *MISS* THAT ONE?

THANK YOU, KOITO-SAN.

THANKS!

Faculty

YEAH.

JUST A *NORMAL* CANDIDATE AND HER *CAMPAIGN MANAGER.*

THANK YOU SO MUCH!

WORKING HARD, EH?

GOOD LUCK!

Approved for Posting

Student Council
Election
Administration
Committee

YEAH...

SEEMS A BIT SOON, DON'T YOU THINK?

SO NANAMI REALLY *IS* RUNNING FOR STUDENT COUNCIL PRESIDENT...

I'M SURE HER FRIEND'S HAPPY ABOUT IT, THOUGH.

Journalism Club

OH, I SEE.

UMM...

I THINK SEEING NANAMI-SENPAI THROUGH MY EYES...

MIGHT HELP *OTHER* FIRST-YEARS GET INTERESTED IN THE ELECTION, TOO.

AH...

Y-YES!

KOITO-SAN, AS CAMPAIGN MANAGER, YOU'RE THE *ONLY* FIRST-YEAR PARTICIPATING IN THE ELECTION, CORRECT?

PHEW...

REALLY? WELL, I DEFINITELY FELT NERVOUS!

GOOD WORK!

INTERVIEWS ARE NERVE-WRACKING, AREN'T THEY?

BUT YOU DIDN'T LOOK NERVOUS AT ALL, SENPAI.

LIAR...

YEAH, BUT YOU'RE PRETTY CONFIDENT, RIGHT?

WINNING THIS ELECTION IS GOING TO BE TOUGH...

EVERY-ONE DEFINITELY GOES ALL-OUT FOR THE ELEC-TIONS...

AND THE OTHER CANDI-DATES ARE AS SERIOUS AS I AM...

AFTER ALL, OUR SCHOOL IS VERY PASSION-ATE ABOUT EVENTS LIKE THIS.

I'M NOT SO SURE--

CANDIDATES AND CAMPAIGN MANAGERS, PLEASE GATHER AROUND!

WE'RE TAKING A GROUP PICTURE!

PLEASE LINE UP OVER THERE!

AH!

SORRY...

SORRY, CAN YOU GET A BIT CLOSER TOGETHER?

OH... IT'S OKAY.

ALL RIGHT, I'M TAKING IT NOW.

SQUEEZE IN JUST A LITTLE MORE, PLEASE!

WE CAN'T!

IT'S NOT FAIR.

BUT THE FACE SHE MADE JUST BECAUSE I GRABBED HER HAND...

I THOUGHT NANAMI-SENPAI WAS LIKE ME...

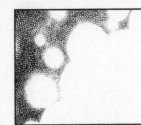

SHE ALREADY **KNOWS** WHAT IT'S LIKE TO FEEL THAT SOMEONE'S "SPECIAL."

I WANT THAT, TOO...

Rustle...

VR22

VR222

I KNOW, I KNOW.

I'M THE ONE WHO KEEPS GETTING MY HOPES UP FOR NOTHING.

SENPAI AND I ARE DIFFERENT.

Nanami Touko

I'd like to go over the speech together soon. Is tomorrow after school okay?

18:21

"SURE, THAT'S FINE." AND... SENT.

WHICH OF YOU ORDERED THE CAFÉ AU LAIT?

AH...

ME.

SENPAI...

SORRY TO KEEP YOU WAITING.

TAKE YOUR TIME AND ENJOY.

KOITO-SAN.

I'M NOT GOING TO ASK YOU TO GO OUT WITH ME.

I KNOW YOU WON'T FALL IN LOVE WITH ME.

BUT THAT'S OKAY.

SO...

I KNOW THAT WE'RE DIFFER-ENT...

JUST LET ME BE IN LOVE WITH YOU.

NH...!

shake
shake

HOW CAN YOU BE IN *LOVE* WITH SOMEONE AND *NOT* WANT THEM TO LOVE YOU *BACK*?

THAT'S...

THAT'S JUST WEIRD.

I'M PERFECTLY CONTENT JUST LIKE THIS.

BUT I DON'T WANT TO GIVE UP WHAT I'M FEELING...

MAYBE IT'S BECAUSE *I* THOUGHT I COULDN'T FALL IN LOVE, EITHER.

IS THAT OKAY?

$$\left(\ \textbf{Bloom Into You}\ \right)$$

WAIT UP! I'M ACTUALLY HEADED THIS WAY, TOO.

HUH? YOU'RE NOT GOING TO THE TRAIN STATION?

WELL, I GUESS I'LL SEE YOU LATER.

I NEED TO STOP BY THE BOOK-STORE.

MY FAMILY'S GOING ON A TRIP OVER BREAK...

SO I WANTED TO GET A BOOK TO READ ON THE WAY.

HOW BIG IS YOUR FAMILY, SENPAI?

IT'S JUST MY PARENTS AND ME, ACTU-ALLY.

RE-ALLY?

OH?

HUH?!

THANKS!

WELCOME HOME, YUU-CHAN.

OH MY!

New Releases

Paperbacks

Paperbacks

WELCOME, WELCOME.

HEE HEE!

WHA--?! WHY DIDN'T YOU MEN-TION THAT SOONER?

OH, ARE YOU SUR-PRISED?

THIS IS MY FAMILY'S STORE.

WELCOME HOME!

THANKS, MOM.

WAIT-- YOUR FAMILY NAME IS KOITO, BUT THE STORE'S CALLED FUJISHIRO BOOKSTORE?

YEAH. IT'S MY GRAND-MOTHER'S.

IT'S LIKE...

"SORRY FOR SEDUCING YOUR DAUGHTER," OR SOME-THING...

UM, YOU HAVEN'T SEDUCED ME, SO...

whisper

UHH, I'M REALLY NERVOUS RIGHT NOW...

WHY? YOU'RE JUST MEET-ING YOUR KOUHAI'S MOM.

WHO'S YOUR FRIEND, YUU?!

?!

YOU'RE JUST AS PRETTY AS YUU SAID!

AH, YES!

I TOLD YOU HOW I'VE BEEN HELPING HER WITH THE SCHOOL ELECTION, RIGHT?

THIS IS NANAMI-SENPAI.

THANKS FOR LOOKING OUT FOR MY DAUGHTER.

BEAM

OH MY! ARE YOU SURE SHE'S NOT A BOTHER?

I'M REALLY LUCKY TO HAVE SUCH A HARD WORKER LIKE KOITO-SAN AT MY SIDE!

NOT AT ALL! SHE'S BEEN A *HUGE* HELP.

WHAT A GREAT SENPAI YOU HAVE!

SHE REALLY SEEMS TO HAVE A GOOD HEAD ON HER SHOULDERS.

CLink CLink

YUU! DON'T BE RUDE TO YOUR SENPAI.

SHE ONLY SEEMS THAT WAY ON THE SURFACE.

Pshhhh

shoop

HEY, I'M HOME.

SO... WHAT'RE YOU ALL TALKING ABOUT?

SHE WAS SO POLITE. IT PUT ME AT EASE!

YOU HAD BETTER TREAT THAT GIRL WELL.

AH HA HA!

NO, WE MET HER SENPAI TODAY--A GIRL.

C'MON, TELL YOUR BIG SISTER!

DON'T TELL ME YUU BROUGHT HOME A BOYFRIEND OR SOMETHING!

WELCOME HOME, REI-CHAN.

......

YEAH, I'M AFRAID I'D HAVE TO PUT MY FOOT DOWN IF IT WAS.

HUH? A GIRL-FRIEND?

NO, IT'S NOT LIKE *THAT...*

IS SHE ASKING YOU TO HANG OUT?

YEAH.

SHE SAYS NATSUKI AND KOYOMI ARE GOING, TOO.

WELL... ALL RIGHT. I WISH YOU'D HELP OUT MORE AT THE STORE, THOUGH.

PI RU RIN

IT'S FROM AKARI.

DON'T USE YOUR PHONE DURING DINNER!

ARE YOU DOING SOFT- BALL AGAIN?

OF COURSE!

IT DOESN'T *HELP* THAT YOU NEVER ANSWER MY TEXTS!

WEEELL, I'M SUPER BUSY WITH CLUB STUFF!

AND AS FOR ME...

I *KNOW*, YOU FOL- LOWED YOUR *SENPAI* INTO THE BASKET- BALL CLUB, *RIGHT?*

HEEEY! RUDE.

YULI, WHAT CLUB DID *YOU* END UP JOIN- ING?

HIGASHI DOESN'T HAVE SOFTBALL, RIGHT?

WHAAT? THAT'S CRAZY!

YULI'S HELPING OUT WITH THE STUDENT COUNCIL INSTEAD OF JOINING A CLUB.

IS THAT OKAY?

A LOVE STORY, HUH?

THIS ONE!

Theater 4

WHICH MOVIE WERE YOU SAYING YOU WANTED TO SEE?

TICKETS

AHHH, THIS WAS SO MUCH FUN!

IT WAS A GOOD MOVIE, HUH?

I THINK THE BOOK WAS A LITTLE BETTER, BUT THE MOVIE WASN'T BAD AT ALL.

MAN, ONCE WE KNEW THEY WERE *BOTH* IN LOVE, I WAS JUST LIKE "CONFESS ALREADY"!

UM... WELL... HE SORTA REJECTED ME ALREADY...

WHICH *REMINDS* ME, AKARI-- WHY *WON'T* YOU JUST CONFESS ALREADY?!

AH...

HUH?

OH GOD, I'M SO SORRY I MADE YOU WATCH A ROMANTIC MOVIE...

C'MON, I SAID IT'S FINE! DON'T MAKE THINGS AWKWARD!

WHAT...?! THAT'S TERRIBLE!

EH, IT'S FINE! DON'T WORRY ABOUT IT.

I'D PROBABLY BE PRETTY UPSET IF HE ALREADY HAD A GIRLFRIEND OR SOMETHING...

BUT HE SAID HE JUST WANTS TO FOCUS ON BASKETBALL RIGHT NOW.

SO IT'S NOT LIKE HE REALLY REJECTED MY FEELINGS.

I KNOW IT SOUNDS WEIRD, BUT I REALLY AM FINE.

THIS ISN'T THE END AT ALL!

I JUST TOLD HIM I'D **WAIT** FOR HIM TO **RETIRE** FROM THE CLUB.

YEAH, EXACTLY, AKARI!

DON'T GIVE UP!

AR-RANGING AND REAR-RANGING THE WORDS ON HER OWN...

OVER AND OVER...

UNTIL SHE FOUND THE PER-FECT ORDER.

AKARI'S SMOOTH **EXPLANATION** SOUNDED LIKE SHE'D **REHEARSED** IT IN ADVANCE.

IF YOU SHOW OFF YOUR **APPEAL** WITHOUT GETTING IN HIS WAY...

YOU MIGHT NOT EVEN HAVE TO **WAIT** UNTIL HE'S OUT!

SOMETIMES LOVE JUST TAKES **TIME** FOR THE OTHER PERSON TO GET INTO, **RIGHT?**

THAT'S **RIGHT!** **WHATEVER** HE SAYS NOW...

YOU **REALLY** THINK SO?

YEAH, OF **COURSE!**

WORK WITH ME HERE!

YOU CAN DO IT!

AFTER ALL, HE DIDN'T TURN YOU DOWN! YOU'VE GOT THIS!

THAT'D BE NICE...

AH...

THANK YOU!

ISN'T YOUR HOUSE ON THE OTHER SIDE OF TOWN?

WHAT BRINGS YOU HERE?

NOTHING! I'M JUST SHOPPING.

I...GOT YOU A SOUVENIR.

ON THE TRIP.

I THOUGHT MAYBE I'D BRING IT TO YOU.

Nn...

I GUESS I JUST FIGURED I'D SEE YOU AT SCHOOL TOMORROW, SO...

THEN WHY DIDN'T YOU JUST WAIT TILL TOMORROW?

YOU SHOULD'VE TEXTED ME BEFORE-HAND OR SOMETHING!

WHAT IF I HADN'T BEEN HOME?

WHAT DO YOU MEAN?

I LOVE YOU, OF COURSE!

SO...

SHE WENT TO SEE THE STARS, HUH?

NEAT.

I MEAN, I DO LIKE STARS.

YEAH... I GUESS I AM.

BUT THAT'S NOT SUR-PRISING.

AM I HAPPY SHE GAVE ME THIS?

WHAT WAS UP WITH *THAT*? SHE NORMALLY DEALS WITH THINGS SO *EASILY*!

Heh.

BUT THAT *FACE* SHE MADE...

ARE YOU *STUPID*, REI-CHAN?

OH, *REALLY?* FROM YOUR *GIRL-FRIEND?*

OH, HEY, **WHAT'S** THIS?

IT WAS A **GIFT.**

YEAH, **SURE,** YOU MEAN YOU LEFT IT AT HIRO-KUN'S, *RIGHT?*

AH! I REACHED THE STARS!

NO, YOU *DIDN'T.*

DON'T BE SILLY.

THERE!

ひょ
hop
ん

"SOMETIMES LOVE JUST TAKES TIME FOR THE OTHER PERSON TO GET INTO, RIGHT?"

I'LL REACH THE STARS, TOO...

I WONDER IF SOME-DAY...

NEXT, I WANT TO GET CHROMODORIS ORIENTALIS- KUN.

THIS IS TRIPANIA NAEVA- SAN.

(Bloom Into You)

5

The One Who Loves Me

EPISODE FIVE

WHY DOES NANAMI-SENPAI *LIKE* ME SO MUCH?

6th period
Election speeches
Voting

"SO I BELIEVE THAT AS THE REPRE-SENTATIVE OF OUR STUDENT BODY...

THE END!

"NANAMI-SENPAI WILL MAKE OUR GREAT SCHOOL *EVEN BETTER.*"

WOW, YOU'VE GOT IT DOWN PAT. I COULD NEVER.

WHAT ARE YOU GOING TO DO ONCE ELECTIONS ARE OVER?

GOOD LUCK!

THINK YOU MIGHT JOIN THE STUDENT COUNCIL?

AND I'VE GOT ALL MY WORRYING OUT OF THE WAY, SO IT'LL BE FINE.

I'VE WRITTEN AND RE-WRITTEN THE SCRIPT SO MANY TIMES...

IN *MIDDLE SCHOOL,* YOU ONLY STARTED SOFTBALL BECAUSE WE MADE YOU...

BUT YOU ENDED UP BECOMING A TEAM REGULAR!

UGH.

NAH, I'M GOOD.

I DUNNO, I THINK YOU'D HAVE FUN IF YOU JOINED, YUU.

I'M NOT JOINING!

YEAH, YOU **REALLY** GET INTO THINGS ONCE YOU GET STARTED.

I MEAN, YOU'VE BEEN WORKING **HARD** WITH THIS ELECTION STUFF, HAVEN'T YOU?

AW, JEEZ... I'M REALLY SWEATING.

DUDE, JUST CALM DOWN.

ARE YOU TWO NERVOUS YET?

HMM... WHO SHOULD I EVEN VOTE FOR?

PROBABLY NANAMI-SENPAI, RIGHT?

I'M GLAD WE GET TO MISS MATH!

UGH, THIS IS A PAIN.

DID YOU COME TO HECKLE US OR BECAUSE YOU'RE WORRIED?

THE FORMER FOR YOU, THE LATTER FOR KOITO-SAN.

SAYAKA!

EVEN IF YOU BOMB IT, TOUKO WILL FIGURE SOMETHING OUT.

GOOD LUCK! YOU'LL BE FINE AS LONG AS YOU RELAX.

HAAA...

WOW, NO PRESSURE OR ANYTHING.

ONLY 'CAUSE I KNOW YOU CAN HANDLE IT, TOUKO.

I'VE BEEN BY HER **SIDE** FOR SO LONG...

AND I'VE **NEVER ONCE** SEEN HER FAIL WHEN THE **STAKES** ARE HIGH.

SAEKI-SENPAI, YOU REALLY HAVE A LOT OF **FAITH** IN TOUKO-SENPAI, HUH?

OF COURSE I DO.

THAT'S **TRUE**... IT'S EASY TO FORGET, BECAUSE SHE'S ALWAYS SO **WEIRD** AROUND ME, BUT...

SHE REALLY IS AN **AMAZING** PERSON.

......

CLINK

MM...

......

UM, I'M GETTING A LITTLE NERVOUS...

IS IT OKAY IF I GO OUTSIDE FOR A MINUTE?

SURE, JUST MAKE SURE YOU'RE BACK BEFORE WE GET STARTED.

OKAY.

SENSEI?

DO YOU THINK YOU COULD COME WITH ME?

ARE YOU ALL RIGHT?

NANAMI-SENPAI...

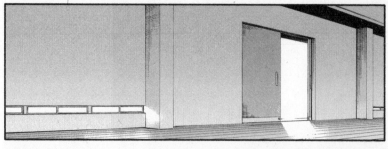

YOU SEEM PRETTY CALM TO ME.

NOT AS CALM AS *YOU* DO.

YOU KNOW...

OH...

THAT'S A RELIEF, THEN.

ME?

YEAH, BUT *I'M* USED TO THIS KIND OF THING.

?

WAIT A MINUTE...

DID YOU COME OUT HERE FOR MY SAKE?

I JUST FIGURED... IF YOU'RE NERVOUS, IT MIGHT BE KIND OF HARD TO ADMIT...

TUG

WANT TO HEAD BACK?

Sigh...

BUT IT SEEMS LIKE I WAS WORRIED FOR NOTHING.

YOU'RE *SHAKING*...

IF YOU'RE *THAT* NERVOUS, WHY DIDN'T YOU TALK TO SAEKI-SENPAI OR SOMEONE?

I THOUGHT I WAS DOING A BETTER JOB OF HIDING IT...

I CAN'T DO THAT.

SAYAKA AND EVERYONE ELSE... THEY ALL BELIEVE IN ME.

I DON'T WANT TO DISAPPOINT THEM...

WHEN I WAS A CHILD...

I DIDN'T STAND OUT AT ALL.

......

WHAT'RE YOU TALKING ABOUT?

MY GRADES WERE AVERAGE, AND I DIDN'T HAVE MANY FRIENDS.

I WAS AFRAID OF **EVERYTHING,** ALWAYS HIDING IN SOMEONE ELSE'S SHADOW.

BUT ONE DAY, I DECIDED I COULDN'T BE LIKE THAT ANY LONGER.

AND LITTLE BY LITTLE...

AS I CHASED AFTER MY IDEAL SELF...

I STUDIED AS MUCH AS I COULD...

I WORKED REALLY HARD TO BE LIKEABLE.

I BECAME WHO I AM TODAY.

......

WHAT MADE YOU DECIDE THAT YOU "COULDN'T BE LIKE THAT ANY LONGER"?

DID SOMETHING HAPPEN...?

YOUR FEELINGS ALWAYS SHOW **RIGHT THROUGH!**

YOU TURN **RED** SO EASILY.

blush

*SELFISHLY MAKING ME YOUR **CAMPAIGN MANAGER**...*

THEN TURNING AROUND AND GETTING NER-VOUS...

IT'S NOT LIKE I EVER SAW YOU AS **PERFECT** IN THE *FIRST* PLACE...

LIKE *EVERYBODY* **ELSE** SEEMS TO.

YOU SHOWING ME YOUR **WEAKER SIDE** IS NOTHING *NEW.*

SO DON'T WORRY.

KOITO-SAN...

?

"NOR-MAL," HM?

OF COURSE YOU'D SAY THAT.

SO...

THIS IS NORMAL.

YOU ALWAYS PUT UP WITH ME, KOITO-SAN.

NOW I SEE...

THAT'S WHY SHE CHOSE ME.

"YES...

"I'M SURE."

"AND YOU'RE SURE YOU DON'T HAVE FEELINGS LIKE THAT FOR ANYONE?"

THAT'S WHAT MAKES ME SPECIAL TO HER.

I LET HER KNOW FROM THE START...

THAT SHE DIDN'T HAVE TO BE ANYTHING SPECIAL IN FRONT OF ME.

I CAN ONLY BE LIKE THIS...

WITH YOU.

EVEN THOUGH SHE'S SO WEAK...

SHE'S STUBBORN AND AWKWARD...

AND SHE FORCES ALL THESE ROLES ON HERSELF.

I'M THE ONLY PERSON WHO SHE CAN TURN TO FOR HELP.

SO...

So that's why...

Phew!

GREAT! SHE GOT THROUGH THE WHOLE THING WITHOUT MESSING UP!

?

Nanami-senpai will make our great school even better.

Throughout this election, Senpai has handled everything perfectly.

To be honest, I started to wonder whether she even needed my help.

I've decided I want to be a student council officer.

But despite that, Senpai showed me that there are plenty of things I can do.

I'M JUST BEING NORMAL...

YOU REALLY ARE BEING NICE TODAY, HUH?

Results of the 47th Student Council President Election

The results of yesterday's student council president election are as follows.

Winner:

Year 2, Class 1
Nanami Touko

Student Council Election
Administration Committee

whisper

I LOVE YOU!

tug

ALL RIGHT, TOUKO, LET THE POOR GIRL GO.

FIIINE.

YEAH, YEAH...

EVEN THOUGH I HAVEN'T **FALLEN IN LOVE** MYSELF...

I'VE GOTTEN **CLOSE** TO THE PERSON WHO **LOVES** ME.

BUT WHAT I DIDN'T **REALIZE** AT THE TIME, WAS THAT BEING NEAR HER...

MEANT I'D HAVE TO **GIVE UP** SOMETHING ELSE.

The new students move to revive the student council play at the cultural festival.

Together, they'll delve into...

Coming Soon!

...their first encounter with love.

LET'S DO IT.

Touko's feelings for Yuu lead to desire.

Desire she can barely control...

HER EYELASHES ARE SO LONG...

Bloom Into You Vol. 2

Afterword

waddle —

I said NIO.

NOT HATO (PIGEON).

Nice to meet you! I'm Nakatani Nio.

bow

THIS IS THE FIRST VOLUME OF MY FIRST SERIES.

Thank you very much for buying the first volume of *Bloom Into You.*

So I hope this name will also grant me a long and successful career as a manga artist.

Coo!

Yeah, right.

fwip

In Shiga, where I'm from, they also call the little grebe the "long-breathed bird"...

"Nio" means "little grebe," a type of bird that can dive underwater for a long time and catch fish. It's the official bird of Shiga prefecture.

So, why did you start drawing **yuri manga**?

You're just going to sit there, aren't you?

Coo coooo?

You just rearranged your real name and came up with "Nio" by mistake.

Then you looked it up in a dictionary a few minutes ago.

Coo coo!

I'm *sorry.* I'd never even seen the kanji for it before!

I WAS TRYING TO LOOK SMART.

SOME KIND OF CONVENTION.

AH, NAKATANI-SAN!

← Editor-san

Just as I was starting to think that to myself...

But I do like yuri, so maybe I should try doing a love story...

Is it right to call my work *yuri* when it's not really about romance?

?

So people already thought of me as a yuri artist.

I've always written stories about relationships between female characters...

YEAH, WE WANNA PRINT SOME YURI!

Fair enough!

I mean, uh, I'd certainly like to, but...

Yuri in *Dengeki Daioh*...?

Hah!

Ta-Daaa!

Yummy Sweets

I'll do it!

ED

NAKATANI-SAN, WOULD YOU LIKE TO DRAW YURI MANGA FOR US?

OH, THIS IS FOR YOU, BY THE WAY.

Yummy Sweets

shake shaake

Thanks!!

☆ My editor, Kusunoki Tatsuya.
☆ Designer-san.
☆ Everyone who helped me with research, storyboard checking, and art checking.
☆ Everyone who was involved with my work in any way.
☆ And thanks to all of you for reading this!

Well, I hope you'll continue to support *Bloom Into You!* Thank you!

And that's how it happened.

That was anti-climactic...

Coo_

Coo_

① Blouse.

Toomi East High School Guide to the Girls' Winter Uniform

② Jumper skirt.

AND A BELT.

SIDE FASTENER.

③ Bolero jacket.

THE FRONT CLOSES WITH A HOOK.

④ Add the ribbon, and you're done!

THERE ARE NO RESTRICTIONS ON THE BAG, SOCKS, OR SHOES.

YOU'RE THE ONLY ONE WHO DOES THAT IN APRIL, AKARI...

IF IT'S TOO HOT, YOU CAN TAKE OFF THE JACKET!

Guide to Ribbon Colors

Students don't get a new one each year; instead, the ribbon colors rotate.

1st years: **Yellow**

2nd years: **Red**

3rd years: **Dark Green**

This Year's Rotation:

1st | 2nd | 3rd

Trapania naeva-san

Bloom into You